Confederate Imprints in the University of Georgia Libraries

Edited by

RICHARD B. HARWELL

UNIVERSITY OF GEORGIA LIBRARIES
MISCELLANEA PUBLICATIONS, NO. 5

UNIVERSITY OF GEORGIA PRESS

ATHENS 1964

Copyright © 1964
University of Georgia Press

Printed in the United States of America
by Printing Department, University of Georgia

Library of Congress Catalog Card Number: 64-22782

Confederate Imprints in the University of Georgia Libraries

WITHDRAWAL

Respectfully dedicated
to the MINUTE MEN of GEORGIA
Secession Quick Step
The SOUTH,
The WHOLE South,
and NOTHING but the SOUTH.
NOLI ME TANGERE!!
by
Herman L. Schreiner
of MACON, Georgia.
also by the same Author:
"Cotton Planters
CONVENTION Schottish."
"JULIA Schottish."
&c. &c.
MACON, GA.
Published by John C. Schreiner & Sons.

Item 81

165714

Ref
Z
1242.5
H315

To

FELIX HARGRETT

Other Publications in the Series

Laws of the Creek Nation
Edited by Antonio J. Waring
No. 1 $1.00

John Howard Payne to His Countrymen
Edited by Clemens de Baillou
No. 2 $2.00

Life and Public Services of an Army Straggler, 1865
By Kittrell J. Warren
Edited by Floyd C. Watkins
No. 3 $2.50 paper; $3.75 cloth

The Journal of a Milledgeville Girl, 1861-1867
Edited by James C. Bonner
No. 4 $3.00

Contents

Foreword

SOON after his graduation from the University of Georgia in 1924, Felix Hargrett began to build an outstanding private library of Southern historical material. As the collection grew in size and historical value, he came to realize that it should be made available to scholars. In time, the purpose of donating it to his *alma mater* was formed. For many years he had sent occasional shipments of books to us but it was not until after our new building was occupied in the fall of 1953—when we had a safe place in which to house rare materials—that he began to make regular donations. Almost every year since then he has made gifts of inestimable value. Time after time he has expressed the hope that his gifts will encourage other alumni and friends to do likewise. I, of course, would be happy for his hopes to be realized.

One of the greatest pleasures in my 36 years as a librarian has been my association with this discriminating collector who knows the contents of his books and their historical value as well as their material worth. Despite a very busy life as an insurance executive, Mr. Hargrett has travelled to countless Southern towns visiting book stores, descendants of famous political figures, lawyers' offices, courthouses—anywhere and everywhere he could locate pieces of Southern Americana, his enduring love. He also is no stranger in the book stores of Boston, New York, Philadelphia, and other cities throughout the country. His success can be gauged by the some 12,000 items which he has collected, most of which are now in the University of Georgia Libraries. Many of them are the only known copies and were rescued from oblivion by him.

Mr. Hargrett's interests are by no means confined to Southern Americana. The materials he has given us range in date from the 15th Century to the present, but the greatest number of pieces bear dates prior to 1865. Many are 18th Century imprints from the presses of the American Colonies and cover a wide range of subjects. One day, a few years ago, he appeared unexpectedly in my office carrying a small but heavy suitcase. After greetings had been exchanged, he said, "I have brought you a few things." Opening the case, he laid upon my desk four incunabula (thereupon doubling our collection of these prized volumes) and almost a hundred Southern pamphlets. Many of the latter were almost as rare as the former.

We appreciate his gifts all the more because we know that he cherishes each item in his collection, and that parting with these old companions not only requires strong determination and self-denial but also costs him a measure of heartache as well. Because of his regard for his treasures, he is reluctant to entrust them to public carriers. Some years he has brought his gift to Athens by car. Other years he has asked me to divide the distance between New York and Athens with him. One year it was Pinehurst, North Carolina; another it was Farmville, Virginia; and still another it was Washington, D. C., where 1,411 publications, mostly Confederate Imprints, were delivered to me under the canopy of a motel during a driving rainstorm. One year, on Christmas Day and in the snow, I filled the trunk of my car with Confederate Imprints and other rarities at his home in Madison, New Jersey, and then drove to Washington over snow-covered roads. He accompanies each consignment of books with a list which he carefully prepares and on which he indicates the rarer volumes. It is in going over these lists that his deep knowledge of books, and historical events and personages, becomes evident. Talking with him about books and book collecting is an education in bibliography, the humanities, and history. Few people know as much about Southern Americana as he.

His donations have enriched our research collections immeasurably. His gifts of Confederate Imprints have made our holdings rank high in comparison with those of other libraries. From him have come 2,067 of the 2,643 pieces in our collection, excluding newspapers and periodicals. The decision was made to include newspapers and periodicals in the list after Mr. Richard Harwell, author of the Introduction, had left Athens. Including them, Mr. Hargrett has presented 2,265 of the 5,667 pieces in the collection.

This publication is being issued in recognition and appreciation of all his donations, but in particular to stress the publications of the Confederate States of America which he has given us. It is indeed appropriate for such a collection as this to be at the University of Georgia, the *alma mater* of Alexander H. Stephens, Robert Toombs, Howell Cobb, and Thomas R. R. Cobb, four Georgians who had much to do with establishing and shaping the government of the Confederate States of America. In the Libraries, Mr. Hargrett's collection will keep company with Thomas R. R. Cobb's copy of the Provisional Constitution and the "permanent" Constitution under which the Confederate central government operated—both are original manuscripts, the latter on parchment.

It is through such friends as Mr. Hargrett that libraries build strong special collections. The University of Georgia is indeed grateful to him for his continued interest and generosity.

My thoughts naturally turned to Richard B. Harwell when we were ready to invite someone to help us organize our Confederate Imprint Collection and to write an introductory essay to this list. Mr. Harwell's active interest in the history and bibliography of the Confederacy is well known. He is without a peer in knowledge of the literature of that era. I am grateful to him for spending almost a week in Athens helping with this project.

I also thank John W. Bonner, Jr., Special Collections Librarian, and Mrs. Susan B. Tate, Library Assistant, Special Collections Division, for spending many hours in the identification and recording of all items, and for writing descriptions of the unlisted titles. They worked long and hard before Mr. Harwell's visit, and were his constant helpers while he was here.

W. Porter Kellam, Director
University of Georgia Libraries

Introduction

COLLECTING books is collecting history. More than that: it is absorbing the life of another era, learning another time as the people who lived in that time knew it. Collecting the books of the Confederacy is the building of a continuing memorial to the Confederates. A book collection is no store-bought statue in a courthouse square, looking younger as each year passes before its stilled and unresponsive gaze. It is a memorial almost living, ever responsive to each new reader because it makes him responsive to the past and to the implications of the past for now and for the future.

Collecting books is the business of a library. But collecting books, cataloging them, and ranging them on shelves is not enough. The fuller business of a library is to bring students and ideas together. It is as the implement of this process that books are collected, cataloged, and shelved. If students and ideas are to be brought efficiently together books must be collected with purpose and wisdom. Special collections in single subject areas must be built as the bases of research on the past and for the future.

It is here one finds the ultimate among the satisfactions of librarianship. Librarians in the mid-twentieth century must be many things other than bookmen—business managers, personnel directors, public relations officers, and (all too often) not-very-glorified janitors. They must be all these things to cope with the complexities of the twentieth-century book world and with the complexities of modern college and university life. But first and always librarians must be bookmen. Libraries are run by administrators, but they are built by bookmen—by bookish librarians and their natural allies, book collectors. Book collectors, however, are not always the allies of librarians. Librarians (at least the good ones) have long ago refuted Randolph Adams's canard that librarians are the enemies of books. There are still too many collectors who are the enemies of the use of books, who collect not to bring students (in college or out) and books together but for pride of possession, who want their books admired rather than read.

Fortunately the library-minded collector and the collecting-minded librarian have met at the University of Georgia in the alliance of Felix Hargrett and Porter Kellam. For years Mr. Hargrett has collected Confederate books. For almost as many years Mr.

Kellam has worked with bringing books and students together. The University has brought Mr. Kellam and Mr. Hargrett together with Mr. Kellam as its Director of Libraries and Mr. Hargrett as a distinguished alumnus and book collector.

Mr. Hargrett's gift of his magnificent collection of Confederate imprints has catapulted the collection of such books at the University into the first rank of libraries of Confederate materials. It is not, however, a simple matter of numerical count. The University of Georgia deserves a collection of this extent and this quality because it is ready for it, because Mr. Hargrett's books can be added to a collection of Confederate imprints already extensive, because the Library already has manuscript collections to supplement books in the study of Confederate history, and because these new additions to the Library can fit into a fully rounded collection of books and other materials about the Confederacy and about the Civil War.

There has been much harping on the unhappy aspects of celebrating the centennial of an event in American history which never should have happened. But it did happen. We cannot ignore our past. We should commemorate—even celebrate—that which is good in our past. This is no time (there is never a time) for reviving old animosities. This is a time for examining our past, learning from it, and passing on an accurate knowledge of it to the future. Too often the past is judged in the glare of hindsight. It is still too difficult to assess the Southern past fairly to our forebears, to ourselves, and to our posterity. Until we can so assess it the Confederacy and its history will have not only a fascination but also a challenge for the compilation of the truthful record.

What I am trying to say, Bishop Atticus G. Haygood said a long time ago. He said it in his remarks at the memorial service in Decatur, Georgia, on December 11, 1889, which marked the death of President Jefferson Davis. Let us *now* hear what he said then, for he was a Confederate in the proper season and he can speak for the Confederates and their short season in history with a reality no historian can approach:

Looking backward is easy, and looking backward some say: "Mr. Davis must have known what the end must be."

People grown up since the war, or brought up elsewhere than in the South before the war, cannot understand what I am going to say. Some who were in the swirl of that tremendous movement will understand me.

How could Mr. Davis know? Who else knew? Call it lunacy, fatuity, judicial blindness, destiny—call it whatever one pleases, this is the truth: Our people did not believe they were going to fail till they were actually falling into the abyss. Their perfect confidence was bottomed on their absolute conviction of the righteousness of their cause and their perfect assurance that Almighty God would vindicate them. Their heroism was matched only by their religion, for when their cause went down in black night and the Confederacy was dead, they accepted the providence that crushed their hope and shocked their faith, and utter failure did not breed unbelief among Southern people.

A weather-wiseman there may have been here and there who knew in 1863 that the war ought to stop; as a rule, a man feathering his nest and making money while his people were bleeding to death, and cool enough to foresee events because he was too selfish to feel the throb of the breaking heart of the Confederacy.

The overwhelming mass of our people did not believe that the war should stop short of absolute independence. Mr. Davis could not in 1863 have stopped the war. [Had] he tried to do it, it would have cost him his head, and have plunged the South into convulsions worse than the war itself. As well speak of stopping a cyclone by incantations.

Let us be just to our heroic dead. He did what we put him at the head of the Confederacy to do. If he thought the war should be pushed to the bitter end, or to independence, so did we all; if not all, yet the most and best of men and women there were.

The night Atlanta fell and the lurid fires lit the very sky, between midnight and day I walked through this old town [Decatur], my home behind me, my family scattered, but I did not believe we were going to fail. "Only a boy's enthusiasm and folly" suggested a cool head of 1889. Not so; our best and wisest felt this strange and invincible confidence. Soldiers in the field, statesmen in the council chamber, ministers of God at the altar, old men and women sending their beardless boys to the front, soldiers, widows and orphans, though cold, hungry and powerless, the men in the trenches, ragged, half fed, barefoot, all felt that we could not fail. Mr. Davis's last message to the Confederate Congress, March 1865, breathes the same spirit. Such a passion of hope and Confidence never before dominated the heart of a whole people.[1]

It is through the books, the magazines, the newspapers, sheet music, texts, government documents, broadsides—all the range of variety of Confederate publications—that collector and librarian can recreate the Confederacy for the present and the historian capture its record for the future. The collecting of the materials of history is no fad, no frivolity, nor mere dilettantism. This we know more fully as our concept of the purposes of libraries and of history be-

1. *The Southern Christian Advocate,* Columbia, S. C., December 19, 1889.

comes more inclusive; but our great-grandfathers knew it too. Warren D. Brown, State Librarian of Alabama, in 1862 addressed a letter to his counterpart in each of the other states of the Confederacy that illustrates Confederate awareness of the importance of collecting the materials of history. He wrote:

> Desiring to procure, for the use of the State Library, all documents, public or private, which will illustrate the history of the war, as well as the proceedings of all deliberative bodies since the war commenced, bearing upon that subject, I have taken the liberty of addressing you in regard to the matter, hoping to obtain your assistance. If convenient, please send to the address of the "State Library, Montgomery, Ala.," such of these documents, susceptible of binding, as you can, and I will reciprocate when opportunity offers.[2]

The collecting of Confederate materials was not systematically maintained during the time of the Confederacy nor immediately afterwards. The times were too much with us. The exigencies of war, the hardships of mere existence during the trying years of Reconstruction militated against the building of libraries. But individuals did collect books, documents, and personal papers and preserved them for later generations to bring together for the use of historians. To them we can be thankful—to Charles Colcock Jones, Jr., of Savannah; to Wymberly Jones DeRenne and Mrs. DeRenne of Wormsloe; to Robert A. Brock of Richmond, and to many others who, if they did not consciously collect, at least did not throw away and, thereby, preserved the materials of history.

Allan Nevins asserts that, no matter how interesting, the history of the Confederacy is of relatively little importance in the great stream of American history, that the existence of the Confederate States was a sort of historical backwash. This may be. But the Confederacy did exist. The more we know about its existence the more we understand not only its own history but the history of the United States. The Confederacy is still too much with us in some of our attitudes as Americans; but those Southerners who understand best the history of the Confederacy also understand best the history of the United States. They know that the Confederacy was not as much outside the mainstream of American history as it was an alternative development of the United States, which, fortunately perhaps, did not command the country's further growth but which was a legitimate result of all that had gone before. The existence of the Confederacy did matter, not just to the Con-

---

2. ALS to Secretary of State of Virginia; Montgomery, September 10, 1862. MS in the Virginia State Library, Richmond.

federates but also to history. It brought about—too violently to be sure, but it did bring about—changes in our philosophy of government that had to come before the United States could grow into the promise of its future. The Confederacy acted as a catalyst on the development of the industrial North and East and on the opening of the West. The difficulty is not that the South fought dishonestly, unreasoningly, or unworthily but that mutual distrust after the war maintained mutual differences long past any excuse for their existence.

Mr. Nevins feels that the drive of the United States was toward a continental empire and that the war only briefly diverted the country from its manifest destiny. Edward A. Pollard, a Confederate editor and historian, made something of the same point when he wrote in early 1865: "When a nation fights for empire there is a limit to its endeavour very far from positive exhaustion. When a nation fights for existence, there is, there should be, no end to the struggle but in the extinction of all its resources."[3] Pollard underestimated the strength of Northern endeavor; he overestimated the extent of Southern resources. In these last few weeks before Confederate defeat he wrote in hope and spirit more than in fact. The "passion of hope and confidence" (as Bishop Haygood phrased it) lasted unbelievably long. "If the cause of the Confederacy is lost," wrote Pollard even as Sherman's army advanced northeastward from Savannah, "it is lost by weak despair; by the cowardice of suicide; by the distress of weak minds. It cannot, CANNOT be lost if the spirit of the people rallies, if dauntless resolution and renewed energy are put against the small and decreasing advantages of the enemy in other respects."[4]

But I am not here to argue Confederate history or to write paeans to a Lost Cause. I am here in my native Georgia on a bookman's holiday from the library of my adoptive college in Maine to help welcome the Hargrett collection of Confederate imprints to the University of Georgia. To see Mr. Hargrett's books, to handle them, to explore among and within them are a delight. Here is the most extensive of private Confederate collections leaving private hands and coming to its permanent home where it will be forever useful to all of the scholarly community. Here is the demonstration of a collector honoring his books, himself, and history by making his collection secure and available in the library of his university.

---

3. *Observations in the North* (Richmond: 1865), p. 132.
4. *Ibid.*, p. 135.

Many old friends among books are here in the Hargrett collection, but there are new friends, too. After twenty-six years of exploration in the field of Confederate books—a field in 1938 almost a *terra incognita*, now well charted—there are still discoveries to be made. This little book alone lists more than a hundred previously unrecorded pieces of Confederate printing, and Mr. Hargrett's collection includes many others which are known only through his copies.

This is not the end of Confederate bibliography. There are known gaps to be filled, and still unsuspected books will yet be discovered. Bibliography is the handmaiden of history, and the writing of Civil War history is far from its end.

Only within the last generation have sectional bitternesses subsided enough that the Civil War can generally be viewed objectively, and too many bitternesses have been unnecessarily revived in the last decade. The full record of the conflict is now very nearly available. Some historian of the future will reassess the whole history of the Confederacy because he will have had access to the whole of its records—in the fine collections at the University of Georgia, at the Boston Athenæum, the New York Public Library, the Library of Congress, the University of Virginia, the Confederate Museum, the Virginia State Library, the Virginia Historical Society, the University of North Carolina, Duke, the University of South Carolina, Emory, the University of Illinois, the Western Reserve Historical Society, the University of Texas, Rice, and the Henry E. Huntington Library. Perhaps in some fine library of the future he can have the materials of all these great libraries brought together on film as a complete record of Confederate printing and, therefore, of Confederate life. There is still much work to be done by bibliographers of the Confederacy before such a library might be possible. Only a handful of Confederate copyright records has survived. These records must, if possible, be filled out, and copies of the books the copyright records list must be located, if possible. It will be a difficult task because Confederate law permitted the advance copyrighting of books that never achieved publication. I am still searching for copies of Albert Welles's *The Doomsday Book; or, Family Register of the Confederate States*, Christopher W. Powell's *Confederate Arithmetic Book for All*, L. G. McMillion's *The Southern Progressive Spelling Book*, and Duval and Martin's *Valuable Receipts for the Soldier, the Housekeeper, the Afflicted, the Farmer, the Merchant, the Manufacturer, &c., &c.*—all copyrighted in Alabama in 1861—*James Waldeen; or, The*

Clouded Heart and Home, by a Young Lady of Mississippi (copyrighted in Alabama, 1863), M. P. Kellogg's *The Practical Spelling Book* and his *The Practical Spelling Book and Definer*, the *Tables of Sterling Exchange* (copyrighted in Georgia, 1863), and various pieces of sheet music known to have been copyrighted but not known in any surviving copies.[5]

One item from the record of "lost" books turns up in Mr. Hargrett's gift to the University of Georgia, *Third Edition of the Bonnie Blue Flag Song Book* (item 79 in this bibliography). Even more exciting to a bibliographer, collector, or librarian is the fact that in the total of the 2,067 items and 2,643 pieces (exclusive of newspapers and periodicals) in the University of Georgia's collection of Confederate imprints there came to it from Mr. Hargrett 96 items and 116 pieces previously unrecorded.

It is not hard to guess why Jeff Weatherford's little *Another Call for Twelve Months Cavalry* (item 56) or Edward Croft's announcement of a *$300 Reward!* for the "foul and unprovoked murder" of Isaac Harrell (item 54) should be excessively rare. It is hard to know why copies of the contemporary printing of Georgia's Ordinance of Secession (item 18) and of the Confederate Senate's printing of *Resolutions Expressive of the Determination of Georgia To Prosecute the Present War with the Utmost Vigor and Energy* (item 1) have never before been recorded.

There is a kind of bibliographical excitement in examining for the first time such important pieces of Western (as well as Southern) Americana as the Confederate States Office of Indian Affairs' *Letter of the Acting Commissioner of Indian Affairs . . . in Regard to Certain Indian Trust Funds* (item 15) or its War Department's *Regulations for the Government of the Forces of the Confederate States in Department of Indian Territory* (item 17). The addition of so many new Georgia items to the list of recorded resources is a particular pleasure and the discovery of still new pieces of sheet music (after I thought I had exhausted that aspect of Confederate bibliography) perhaps a bit of embarrassment. There is relatively little among the new items of great importance. What they add to Confederate history is corroborative rather than new, but this does not lessen their value. The record should be as full as possible.

In its first issue the editors of *The Southern Illustrated News* wrote:

---

5. These items are mentioned in the Confederate copyright records preserved as part of the Pickett Papers, Manuscripts Division, Library of Congress.

In the nature of things . . . [with] a people begirt by enemies, in the midst of a war unexampled in history for the ferocity with which it has been carried on by their assailants and the infernal purposes these assailants have not hesitated to avow, mere literary or artistic novelties cannot be very popular. When the wolf is at the door the family cannot enjoy the "Cotter's Saturday Night." The minds of men are too much preoccupied by the stirring events of the hour to be amused with the situations of the novelist or beguiled by the fancies of the poet. There is a deeper pathos, a loftier poetry in the incidents of yesterday's battlefield than belongs to the most tuneful measure, while Jack Morgan and Jeb. Stuart surpass all the knighthood of romance.[6]

Time has cloaked the Confederacy in too much romance. But the printed materials of a century ago are an antidote to unwarranted romanticizing. They are the tools of history, not of romance; of truth, not fiction. The reality of them and the reality a study of them gives to Confederate history still hold that deeper pathos, that loftier poetry. In the printed records of the Confederacy is the living memorial to the Confederacy.

Richard Harwell

Athens, Georgia
March 13, 1964

6. Richmond, September 13, 1862.

Previously Unrecorded Confederate Imprints

Confederate States of America Official Publications

SENATE

Bills, resolutions, etc.

1*

. . . Resolutions expressive of the determination of Georgia to prosecute the present war with the utmost vigor and energy. [Richmond, 1864.] 2 p. 24½ cm.

Caption title.

Senate, January 8, 1864. — Read and ordered to be printed. <Presented by President pro tempore.>

ARMY

Department no. 2

2

General orders, no. 94. [Tupelo, Miss., 1862.] 2 p. 21 cm.

Dated: Head Quarters, Department no. 2, Tupelo, Miss., July 8th, 1862.
Signed: By command of General Bragg. Thomas Jordan, Chief of Staff.

Department of East Tennessee

3

Circular. [Bristol, Va., 1864.] Broadside, 30 x 12½ cm.

Dated: Head Quarters Dept. of E. Tenn., April 30th, 1864.
Signed: By command of Maj. General Buckner, J. N. Galleher, A.A.G.

4

General orders. [Abingdon, Va., 1864.] v. p. 24½ cm.

Nos. 5-8; April 29-30, 1864.
Nos. 6-8 dated at Bristol.
No. 7 measures 29½ cm.

---

*Items marked with an asterisk denote gifts by Felix Hargrett.

Department of Georgia. Post at Dahlonega

5

To the people of northern and northeastern Georgia and south western North Carolina. . . . General order no. 1 . . . [signed:] G. W. Lee, commanding. [Dahlonega, 1863.] Broadside, 30½ x 13½ cm.

Dated: Headquarters, Dahlonega, Ga., January 26th, 1863.

Department of Mississippi and East Louisiana

6

General orders no. 24. [Brandon, Miss., 1863.] Broadside, 10 x 19½ cm.

Dated: Head Quarters, Brandon, Miss., December 22d, 1863.

Signed: J. E. Johnston, General. Official. Benj. S. Ewell, A. A. General.

7

Special orders, no. 211 . . . [Meridian, Miss., 1863.] Broadside 25 x 20 cm.

Dated: Head Quarters, Meridian, Miss., October 11, 1863.

Signed: By command of Gen. Johnston, Benj. S. Ewell, A. A. Gen'l.

Department of North Carolina

8*

General orders. [Petersburg, Va., 1863.] v. p. 22 cm.

Nos. 10, 16; November 7, December 15, 1863.

Department of Western Virginia. Post at Charleston

9

General order no. 2 . . . [Charleston, Va., 1861.] Broadside. 20 x 12 cm.

Dated: Charleston, Va., 12th Nov., A.D. 1861.

Signed: By order of E. B. Tyler, Col. Commanding Post. D. H. Brown, A. S. Major.

Department of Western Virginia and East Tennessee

10

General orders. [Dublin, Va., 1864.] v. p. 23 cm.

Nos. 1, 3-8, 10, 12; January 7, 19, 29, February 1, 2, 7, 9, 25, and 29, 1864.

No. 10 is numbered in manuscript.

Nos. 3 and later dated only as from Department of Western Virginia.

District of Texas, New Mexico, and Arizona

11

Special orders. [Houston, Tex., 1864.] v. p. 20½ cm.

Nos. 27, 118; January 27, April 28, 1864.

Western Sub-District of Texas

12

General order, no. 8. . . . [Fort Brown, Tex., 1863.] Broadside, 20 x 13½ cm.

Dated: Head Quarters, Western Sub-District of Texas, Fort Brown, Feb. 16th, 1863.

Signed: Brig. Gen. H. P. Bee. By order of E. F. Bray, Major & A. A. A. Gen.

CONSCRIPT DEPARTMENT

13

. . . General orders, no. 8 . . . [Rusk, Tex., 1864.] Broadside, 18½ x 7½ cm.

Dated: Hd. Qr's. Conscript Service, District of Texas, Rusk, June 8th, 1864.

Signed: By order of D. B. Martin, Co., & Com'd, Conscripts, Dist. of Texas. Sam. A. Willson, Capt. & Adj't.

14

General orders, no. 9. . . . [Rusk, Tex., 1864.] Broadside, 12 x 8 cm.

Dated: Hd. Qr's. Conscript Service, District of Texas, Rusk, June 10th, 1864.

Signed: By order of D. B. Martin, Col. & Comd. Conscripts, Dist. of Texas. Sam. A. Willson, Capt. & Ad'jt. [*sic*]

OFFICE OF INDIAN AFFAIRS

15

Letter of the acting commissioner of Indian affairs, with statement, &c. in regard to certain Indian trust funds. January 17, 1862. Richmond: Ritchie and Dunnavant, Printers. 1862. 12 p. 19 cm.

WAR DEPARTMENT

16

Circular. . . . [Concerning commutation money for clothing. Richmond. 1861.] Broadside, 25½ x 20 cm.

Dated: Quartermaster General's Department . . . September 30, 1861.

Signed: A. C. Myers, Quartermaster General.

17

Regulations for the government of the forces of the Confederate States in Department of Indian Territory. Part II. Respecting the rights, duties, and business of the officer and soldier. Promulgated at Fort McCulloch, 1st July, 1862. [Fort McCulloch, Indian Territory, 1862.] 36 p. 20½ cm.

Bound in book endpapers.

Official Publications of the Separate States

GEORGIA

Convention

18*

An ordinance to dissolve the union between the State of Georgia and the other states united with her, under the compact of government entitled the Constitution of the United States: . . . Passed at Milledgeville, Ga., January 19, 1861. [Milledgeville, 1861.] Broadside, 35 x 21½ cm.

General Assembly

19

. . . An act to amend an act entitled an act to provide for the public defense, and for other purposes, assented to December 16, 1861. [Milledgeville, 1862?] Broadside, 17½ x 11 cm.

At head of title: From the Waters' pamphlet. (No. 49.).

Governor

20

. . . [Letter to] Ira R. Foster, Q. M. G. . . . [Signed:] Joseph E. Brown. [Milledgeville, 1863.] Broadside, 24½ x 20½ cm.

Dated: Executive Department, Milledgeville, May 27, 1863.

At end are Resolutions of the General Assembly of Georgia, assented to 15th April, 1863.

Adjutant General

21

[Circular.] . . . Gilham's Manual for volunteers and militia having been approved by the Commander-in-Chief, he orders that it be issued to the volunteers and militia of the State of Georgia for their government, and that it be strictly adhered to. . . . [Signed:] Henry C. Wayne, Adjutant Gen'l. [Milledgeville, 1861.] Broadside, 19 x 12 cm.

Dated: Executive Department, Adjutant General's Office, Feb'y 1, 1861.

22

Circular . . . [Milledgeville, 1861.] Broadside, 21½ x 14 cm.

Dated: Executive Department, Milledgeville, Ga., Feb'y 19th, 1861.

Signed: By order of the Commander-in-Chief. D. R. Jones [in manuscript], Asst. Adjt. General.

$300 REWARD!

A foul and unprovoked murder was committed last night upon James Smith, a volunteer soldier of my company, by ISAAC HARRELL, who kept a Doggery at the foot of Womack's Hill.

Said Harrell is about 50 years of age, 6 feet high, light thin and greyish hair, dissipated look, rather red complexion, dressed slovenly, dark grey pants, side stripes, new black satinet vest, and common coat. I will give $100 for his delivery, and have written to the Governor, who will doubtless offer the usual reward of $200 for his apprehension.

EDWARD CROFT, Captain.

Columbus, Ga., November 11, 1861.

Item 54

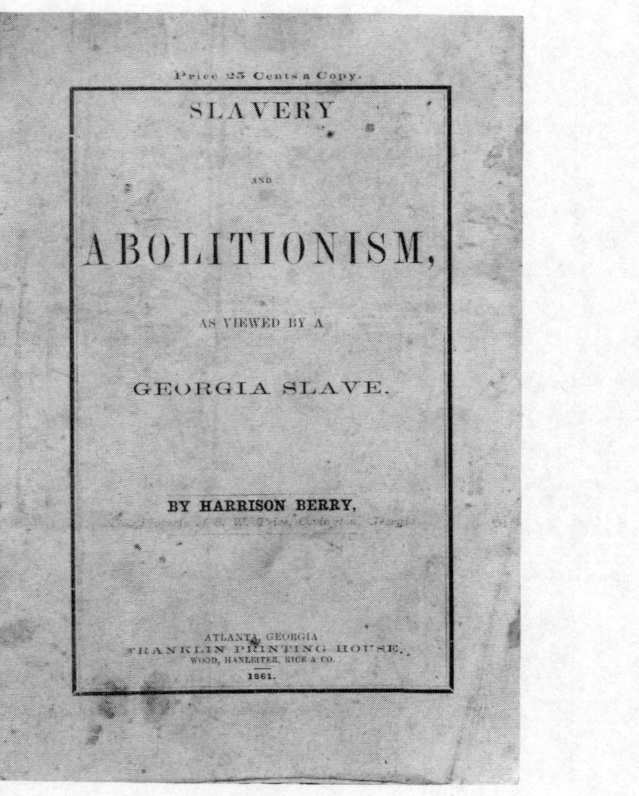

Price 25 Cents a Copy.

SLAVERY

AND

ABOLITIONISM,

AS VIEWED BY A

GEORGIA SLAVE.

BY HARRISON BERRY,

ATLANTA, GEORGIA:
FRANKLIN PRINTING HOUSE,
WOOD, HANLEITER, RICE & CO.
1861.

Crandall 2882

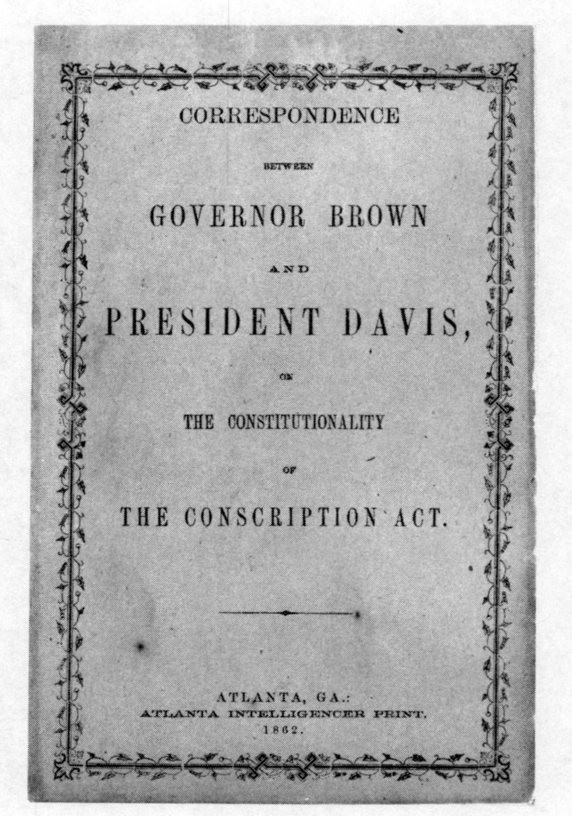

CORRESPONDENCE

BETWEEN

GOVERNOR BROWN

AND

PRESIDENT DAVIS,

ON

THE CONSTITUTIONALITY

OF

THE CONSCRIPTION ACT.

ATLANTA, GA.:
ATLANTA INTELLIGENCER PRINT.
1862.

Crandall 1563

CATALOGUE

OF

IMPORTED GOODS,

TO BE SOLD AT AUCTION,

BY JAMES H. TAYLOR,

At 296 Broad Street, Augusta, Ga.,

On Wednesday Morning, March 23d, 1864,

SALE COMMENCING AT TEN O'CLOCK.

CONDITIONS CASH, IN CONFEDERATE FUNDS.
NO PACKING WILL BE DONE

AUGUSTA, GA.:
STEAM PRESS CHRONICLE & SENTINEL
1864.

Item 72

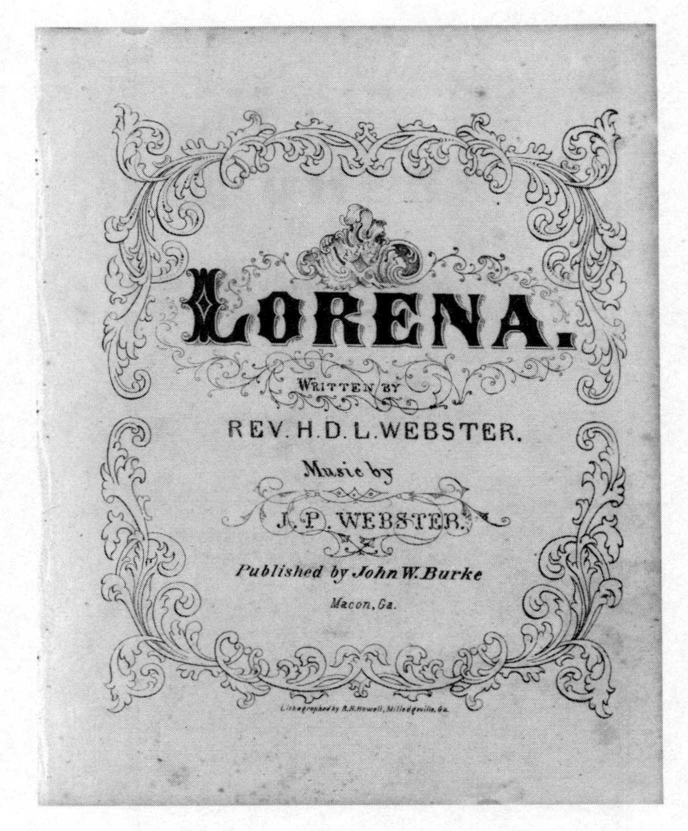
LORENA.

WRITTEN BY

REV. H. D. L. WEBSTER.

Music by

J. P. WEBSTER.

Published by John W. Burke

Macon, Ga.

Lithographed by R.H. Howell, Milledgeville, Ga.

Item 82

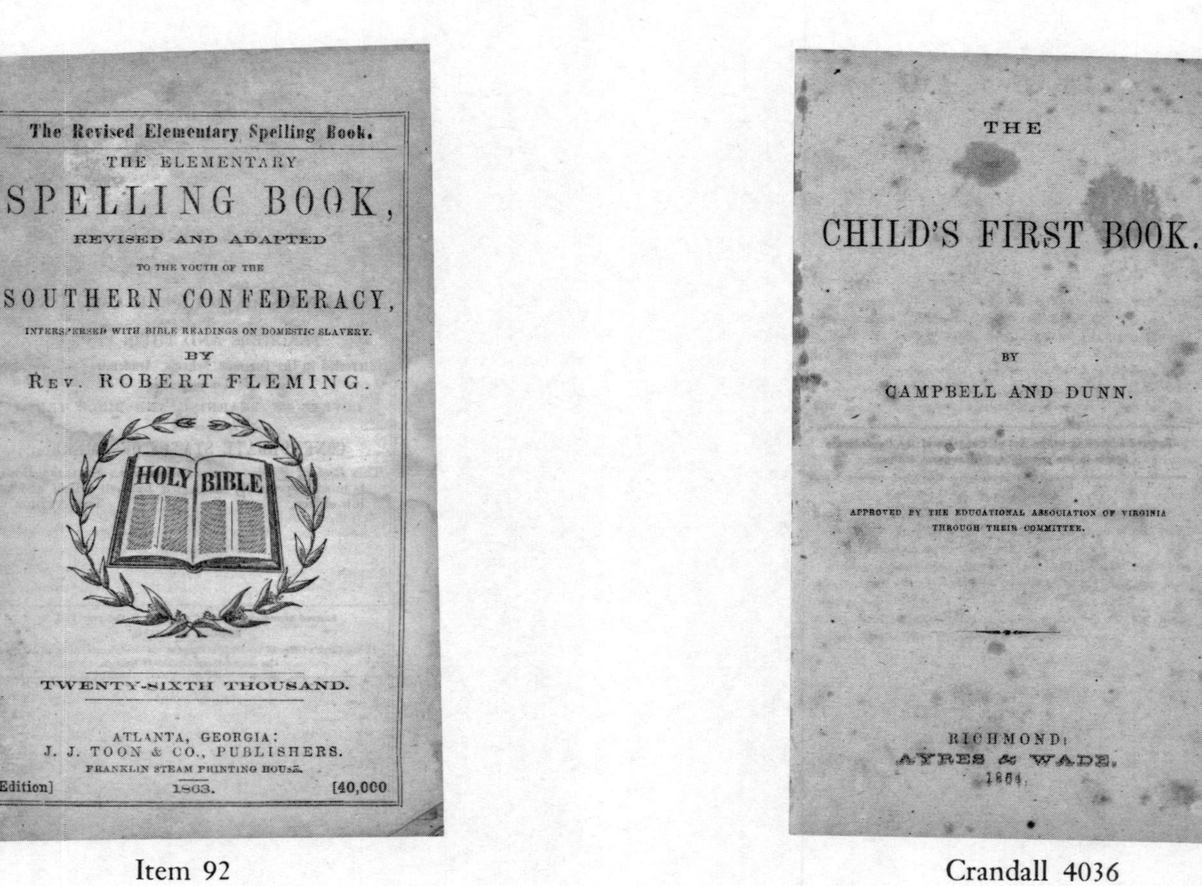

The Revised Elementary Spelling Book.

THE ELEMENTARY

SPELLING BOOK,

REVISED AND ADAPTED

TO THE YOUTH OF THE

SOUTHERN CONFEDERACY,

INTERSPERSED WITH BIBLE READINGS ON DOMESTIC SLAVERY.

BY

REV. ROBERT FLEMING.

TWENTY-SIXTH THOUSAND.

ATLANTA, GEORGIA:
J. J. TOON & CO., PUBLISHERS.
FRANKLIN STEAM PRINTING HOUSE.

Edition] 1863. [40,000

Item 92

THE

CHILD'S FIRST BOOK.

BY

CAMPBELL AND DUNN.

APPROVED BY THE EDUCATIONAL ASSOCIATION OF VIRGINIA
THROUGH THEIR COMMITTEE.

RICHMOND:
AYRES & WADE.
1864.

Crandall 4036

23

[Circular.] . . . In view of the present trouble by which we are surrounded, it becomes necessary that all the arms belonging to the state go into the hands of men who are willing to enter the service *for the war*, as now required by law, and as the company you command has received arms from the state, you are required, either to tender the services of your company, (to consist of not less than fifty nor more than eighty rank and file,) for service during the war, or to return the arms and equipments in its possession to the arsenal at this place, that they may be placed in the hands of some of the numerous companies already tendered for the war. . . . [Signed:] By order of the Commander-in-Chief: Henry C. Wayne, Adj. & Ins. General. [Milledgeville, 1861.] Broadside, 20 x 12½ cm.

Dated: Executive Department, Adjutant General's Office, Milledgeville, Ga., June 19th, 1861.

ALs of William Grisham, Canton, Ga., January 20, 1864, on attached blank leaf and in margins.

24

. . . [Circular letter enclosing Governor Joseph E. Brown's] Proclamation of the 11th [February] and General order no. 2 [concerning the enrolling of new troops. Signed:] Henry C. Wayne, Adj. & Ins. General. [Milledgeville, 1862.] Broadside, 27½ x 21 cm.

Dated: State of Georgia, Adjutant and Inspector General's Office, Milledgeville, Ga., February 17, 1862.

25

Circular . . . Instructions for claimants against the state for guns furnished and not paid for or returned. . . . [Signed:] Henry C. Wayne, Adjutant and Inspector General. [Milledgeville, 1863.] Broadside, 33½ x 21 cm.

Dated: State of Georgia. Adjutant and Inspector General's Office, Milledgeville, April 23d, 1863.

26

[Circular letter acknowledging receipt of application for exemption. Signed:] Henry C. Wayne, Adjutant & Inspector General. [Milledgeville, 1864.] Broadside, 21 x 12½ cm.

Dated: State of Georgia. Adjutant and Inspector General's Office, Milledgeville, [ ] 1864.

27

General orders. [Milledgeville, 1861.] v. p. 22 cm.

Nos. 5, 7, 8; February 20, May 8, 14, 1861.

28

. . . General orders, no. 24. . . . [Milledgeville, 1862.] Broadside, 23½ x 11½ cm.

Dated: State of Georgia. Adj't and Inspect'r Gen's Office, Milledgeville, Dec. 27th, 1862.

Signed: By order of the Commander-in-Chief; Henry C. Wayne, Adj't and Ins. Gen.

29

General orders. [Milledgeville, 1864.] v. p. 25 cm.

Nos. 14, 21, 24, 28, 30, 31; April 18, August 17, October 6, 12, 13, and 15, 1864.

Nos. 21 and 31 are printed on a single fold of paper.

Commissary General

30*

Annual report of Jared I. Whitaker, Commissary General of Georgia, for the fiscal year, ending October 15th, 1863. Milledgeville, Ga.: Boughton, Nisbet, Barnes & Moore, State Printers. 1863, 6 p., 1 l, 15 p. incl. tables. 23 cm.

31

Regulations for the Commissariat of the State of Georgia. 1861. Milledgeville, Ga.: Boughton, Nisbet & Barnes, State Printers. 1861. 43 p. incl. forms. 23 cm.

Bound with Regulations for the Quartermaster's Department of the State of Georgia. 1861. Milledgeville, Ga.: Boughton, Nisbet & Barnes. 1861. See No. 37.

Comptroller General

32

Annual circular. . . . [Milledgeville, 1863.] 2 p. 52 x 22 cm.

Dated: Comptroller General's Office, Milledgeville, February 28, 1863.

Signed: Peterson Thweatt, Comptroller General.

33

Annual report of the Comptroller General of the State of Georgia, made to the Governor, October 21, 1862. Milledgeville, Ga.: Boughton, Nisbet & Barnes, State Printers. 1862. 140 p. incl. tables. 21½ cm.

Militia

34

General orders, no. 6. . . . [Griffin, Ga., 1862.] Broadside, 23½ x 15 cm.

Dated: Head-Quarters, Camp Stephens, March 24th, 1862.

Signed: M. C. Fulton, A. D. C.

35

General order, no. IV. . . . [Atlanta, 1864.] Broadside, 33 x 17 cm.

Dated: Headquarters Georgia Militia, Atlanta, Ga., May 25, 1864.

Signed: Henry C. Wayne, Major General.

Printed in two columns.

36

General orders, no. 9. . . . [Atlanta, 1864.] Broadside, 14½ x 11½ cm.

Dated: Head Quarters Georgia Militia, Atlanta, June 2d, 1864.
Signed: By command of Major General, Henry C. Wayne. W. K. DeGraffenreid, Maj. and A. A. General.

Quartermaster's Department

37

Regulations for the Quartermaster's Department of the State of Georgia. 1861. Milledgeville, Ga.: Boughton, Nisbet & Barnes, State Printers. 1861. 80 p. 23 cm.

Bound with this is Regulations for the Commissariat of the State of Georgia. 1861. Milledgeville, Ga.: Boughton, Nisbet & Barnes, State Printers, 1861.
Cover title: Regulations for the Quartermaster's Department and Commissariat of the State of Georgia. 1861.
Two copies; one bound in green paper, one in blue.

Supreme Court

38

Reports of cases in law and equity, argued and determined in the Supreme Court of the State of Georgia, including the August term, 1860, at Atlanta; the November term, 1860, at Milledgeville; the November term, 1860, at Athens; and part of the January term, 1861, at Savannah. Volume XXXI. By George N. Lester, reporter. Atlanta, Ga.: Franklin Printing House. Wood, Hanleiter, Rice & Co. 1861. vii, 805 p. 22½ cm.

Augusta

39

Proceedings of a public meeting of the citizens of Augusta, called by the mayor to consider the defences of the city against the public enemy. Augusta, Ga.: Steam Press of Chronicle & Sentinel. 1862. 8 p. 24½ cm.

Columbus

40

Standing committees for 1861. . . . [Columbus, Ga., 1861.] Card. 5½ x 8½ cm.

LOUISIANA

Legislature

41

An act, to authorize the Governor to raise troops for the defence of the state, by voluntary enlistment . . . [Shreveport? 1863.] Broadside, 13 x 13 cm.

Approved June 20, 1863.

42

The militia law of June 20th, 1863. . . . [Shreveport? 1863.] Broadside, 46 x 31½ cm.

Approved June 20, 1863.
Printed in three columns.

Louisiana State Forces

43

Ordnance rules and regulations. . . . [Alexandria, 1863.] Broadside, 34 x 21½ cm.

Dated: Headquarters, Louisiana State Forces, Office of the Chief of Ordnance, Alexandria, August 15th, 1863.
Signed: Sam'l. McCutcheon, Major and Chief of Ordnance.

Supreme Court

44

Decision of the Supreme Court. The State of Louisiana, on the application of Gabriel G. Norton for a writ of habeas corpus, vs. Captain Benjamin Bickham, successor in office to Capt. Wm. Flournoy. . . . [Shreveport? 1863.] [2] p. 45½ cm.

Printed in four columns.

NORTH CAROLINA

General Assembly

45

Resolutions vindicating the loyalty of the state of North-Carolina and its General Assembly. . . . [Raleigh, 1863.] Broadside, 25½ x 20½ cm.

<Read and ratified in General Assembly, this 30th day of January, A.D., 1863.>

Governor

46

. . . [Circular letter enclosing] a series of resolutions passed by the Legislature of Tennessee, in relation to a congress of the banks of the Southern states. . . . [Raleigh, 1861.] 2 l. 25½ x 20 cm.

Dated: State of North Carolina, Executive Department, Raleigh, July 1st, 1861.
Signed: John W. Ellis.
Second leaf reprints "Joint resolutions providing for a bank congress of the Southern States. Resolved by the General Assembly of the State of Tennessee . . . Passed May 8, 1861."

Supreme Court

47*

. . . Reports of cases in law, argued and determined in the Supreme Court of North Carolina, June term, 1862. Vol. VIII. By Hamilton C. Jones, reporter. Salisbury, N. C.: Printed by J. J. Bruner. 1862.

SOUTH CAROLINA

Convention

48*

An ordinance, to dissolve the union between the State of South Carolina and other states united with her under the compact entitled, "The constitution of the United States of America." . . . Charleston, Evans & Cogswell, Printers. [1860?] Card, 20½ x 13½ cm.

Text printed within decorative border; palmetto flag at head of text.

General Assembly

49

An act to provide for a guaranty by the State of the bonds of the Confederate States . . . [Columbia, 1863.] 2 l. 24 cm.

Dated December 18, 1862.

First leaf is covering letter signed and addressed in manuscript from Governor M. L. Bonham to Governor Joseph E. Brown of Georgia transmitting the copy of the act. Dated: The State of South Carolina, Executive Department, Columbia, January 15th, 1863.

50

An act to provide for a guaranty by the State of the bonds of the Confederate States . . . [Columbia, 1863.] 2 l. 32½ cm.

Dated February 6, 1863.

The act is followed by resolutions of the Senate and House requesting the Governor to communicate it to the Confederate Congress and to the governors of the several Confederate states.

First leaf is covering letter signed and addressed in manuscript from Governor M. L. Bonham to Governor Joseph E. Brown of Georgia transmitting the copy of the act. Dated: Executive Department, Columbia, S. C., February 9, 1863.

51*

Reports and resolutions of the General Assembly of the State of South Carolina, passed at the annual session of 1860. Columbia, S. C.: R. W. Gibbes, State Printer. 1860. 535 p. incl. tables, 23 cm.

Includes material dated 1861.

House of Representatives

52*

Journal of the House of Representatives of the State of South Carolina: being the sessions of 1860. Columbia, S. C.: R. W. Gibbes, State Printer. 1860. 493, [1] p. 25 cm.

The journal continues through January 28, 1861.

Unofficial Publications

MILITARY, HISTORICAL, AND ECONOMIC PUBLICATIONS

Military Miscellanies

53

"Bena," *pseud.*

Thoughts on our army. . . . [Richmond: Macfarlane & Fergusson, Printers. n. d.] 8 p. 20½ cm.

Caption title.

Wall-paper covers.

54

Croft, Edward

$300 reward! A foul and unprovoked murder was committed last night upon James Smith, a volunteer soldier of my company, by Isaac Harrell, who kept a doggery at the foot of Womack's Hill. . . . [Columbus, Ga., 1861.] Broadside, 21½ x 37½ cm.

55

Munroe, N. C.

[Circular letter requesting contributions to help build an iron battery at Savannah. Macon, Ga., 1862.] Broadside, 21 x 14 cm.

Dated: Macon, Ga., April 2nd, 1862.

Signed: N. C. Munroe, Isaac Scott, James A. Nisbet, John B. Ross, William B. Johnston, Commitee.

56

Weatherford, Jeff

Another call for twelve months cavalry . . . [Lancaster, Tex., 1862.] Broadside, 22 x 8½ cm.

Dated: Lancaster, Texas. April 15, 1862.

History

57*

The Chickahominy fight thus far. . . . [Richmond? 1862.] Broadside. 26½ x 12 cm.

58

Hayne, Paul Hamilton

M. M. S. [*sic*] of volume first of the work entitled "Politics of South Carolina, F. W. Pickens' speeches, reports, &c." By Paul H. Hayne. . . . [Columbia, 1865?] 104 p. 24½ cm.

Unbound sheets of a volume apparently never completed. The text ends abruptly at p. 104.

59*

Jackson, Henry W. R.

Historical register, and Confederates assistant to national independence. Containing a discovery for the preservation of butter, together with other valuable recipes and important information for the soldier, and the people in general throughout the Confederate States of America. . . . By H. W. R. Jackson. Augusta, Ga.: Printed at the Office of the Constitutionalist. 1862. 44 p.

Advertisement on verso of cover-title. Advertisement on both sides of back wrapper.

Business and Agriculture

60

Atkinson, G. W., & Co., Columbus, Georgia

[Circular advertisement:] We beg leave to call your attention to our extensive stock of staple and fancy dry goods . . . [Columbus, Ga., 1861.] Broadside, 27½ x 21 cm.

Dated: Columbus, Georgia, April 17, 1861.

61

Baylor, C. G.

To his excellency, Joseph E. Brown, Governor of Georgia . . . [n. p., 1861.] 27 p. incl. tables. 21½ cm.

Caption title.

A report to Governor Brown on the foreign cotton trade.

62

Bruce, E. M.

. . . To the planters of the South. . . . I avail myself of this opportunity to advise you that I have made ample provision for salt, cooperage, &c., to pack fifteen to twenty (15 to 20,000) thousand head of cattle, and thirty to fifty (30 to 50,000) thousand hogs, (have large and complete packing houses,) in this city, and will be prepared to fill order for prime or mess beef, rounds, tongues, &c., any time after 15th October . . . [Signed:] E. M. Bruce, Nashville, Tenn. [Nashville, 1861.] Broadside, 27½ x 21½ cm.

Dated: Nashville, Tenn., Sept. 20, 1861.

At head of title: Please post up and hand to your planters!

63

Cobb, Howell

To the planters of Georgia. . . . [Signed:] Howell Cobb, Thos. R. R. Cobb. . . . [n. p., 1861.] Broadside, 54 x 14 cm.

An appeal for subscriptions of cotton to be exchanged for Confederate bonds. Followed by act of Congress authorizing the loan.

Printed in two columns.

64

[Culver, C. P.]

The Southern telegraph. [n. p., 1863.] 10 p. 21½ cm.

Caption title.

Signed and dated: C. P. Culver. Berzilia, Ga., April 13, 1863.

65

Eagle Manufacturing Company, Columbus, Ga.

Condition of the Eagle Manufacturing Company, Columbus, Georgia, February 1st, 1861. . . . [Columbus, Ga., 1861.] Broadside, 31½ x 21½ cm.

At end is: Circular to the stockholders of the Eagle Manufacturing Company. Dated: Columbus March 4th, 1861. Signed: John. McGough, Secretary.

66

Eagle Manufacturing Company, Columbus, Ga.

Condition of the Eagle Manufacturing Company, Columbus, Georgia, August 1st, 1861. . . . [Columbus, Ga., 1861.] Broadside, 27 x 21 cm.

At end is: Circular to the stockholders.

Dated: Columbus, Georgia, August 10th, 1861. Signed: Wm. H. Young, Secretary.

67

Georgia Railroad

Notice to parties contracting for wood and ties, on line of Georgia rail road, for February and March, 1862. . . . [Signed:] P. W. Printup, Inspector. [Augusta, Ga.? 1862.] Broadside, 19 x 15½ cm.

68

Memorial of the banks of Savannah. Savannah, Purse, Printer [1864] 3 p. 33½ cm.

Title on verso of p. 3.

Caption title: To the honorable the Senate and House of Representatives of the Confederate States. The memorial of the banks of the city of Savannah – showeth: . . .

Signed: G. B. Lamar, President Bank of Commerce; W. Thorne Williams, President *pro. tem.* Bank State Georgia, Jno. Richardson, President Farmers' and Mechanics' Bank; A. Champion, President of the Marine Bank of Georgia; Geo. W. Anderson, President Planters' Bank.

69

Public meeting in Greenesboro. "All corn – no cotton to be planted." . . . [Greenesboro, Ga.? 1862.] Broadside, 26½ x 16½ cm.

Includes preamble and resolutions adopted at a public meeting held March 15, 1862 at the request of the grand jury of Greene county.

70

Taylor, James H.

Catalogue of imported goods, per steamer Douro and other steamers, to be sold at auction, by James H. Taylor, at his sales room,

PRINCIPLES AND MAXIMS

OF THE

ART OF WAR;

OUTPOST SERVICE;

GENERAL INSTRUCTIONS FOR BATTLE;

REVIEWS.

CHARLESTON:
STEAM-POWER PRESS OF EVANS & COGSWELL,
No. 3 Broad and 103 East Bay streets.
1863.

Crandall 2395

REGULATIONS

FOR

THE GOVERNMENT OF THE FORCES

OF

THE CONFEDERATE STATES

IN

DEPARTMENT OF INDIAN TERRITORY.

PART II.

Respecting the Rights, Duties, and Business of the Officer and Soldier.

PROMULGATED AT FORT McCULLOCH, 1st JULY,

1862.

Item 17

AN ORDINANCE

To Dissolve the Union between the State of Georgia and the other States united with her, under the compact of Government entitled the Constitution of the United States:

We, the people of the State of Georgia, in Convention assembled, do declare and ordain, and it is hereby declared and ordained, that the Ordinance adopted by the people of the State of Georgia, in the Convention of 1788, whereby the Constitution of the United States was ratified and adopted, and also all acts and parts of acts of the General Assembly, ratifying and adopting amendments to the said Constitution, are hereby repealed, rescinded, and abrogated.

We do further declare and ordain, that the Union now subsisting between the State of Georgia and the other States, under the title of the United States of America, is hereby dissolved, and that the State of Georgia is in the full possession and exercise of all those rights of sovereignty which belong and appertain to a free and independent State.

Passed at Milledgeville, Ga., January 19, 1861.

Item 18

W. B. Griffin & Co., auctioneers, on Friday, November 6, '63, commencing at 9 o'clock. Conditions – cash in bankable funds. Accuracy of catalogue not warranted. No packing done in the house. Augusta, Ga.: Steam Press Chronicle & Sentinel. 1863. 12 p. 27½ cm.

71

Taylor, James H.

Catalogue of imported goods, per steamers Syren, Druid & Fox, and consignments by other vessels, to be sold at auction, by James H. Taylor, at 296 Broad street, Augusta, Ga., on Wednesday morning, September 28th, 1864, sale commencing at nine o'clock. Conditions cash. No packing will be done. Augusta, Ga.: Steam Press Chronicle & Sentinel. 1864. 18 p. 27½ cm.

72

Taylor, James H.

Catalogue of imported goods, to be sold at auction, by James H. Taylor, at 296 Broad Street, Augusta, Ga., on Wednesday morning, March 23d, 1864, sale commencing at ten o'clock. Conditions cash, in Confederate funds. No packing will be done. Augusta, Ga.: Steam Press Chronicle & Sentinel. 1864. 9 p. 27½ cm.

73

Wright & Jackson, Savannah

Dissolution of copartnership [of Wm. B. Jackson & Co.] . . . Copartnership notice [of Wright & Jackson. Savannah, 1861.] [3] p. 21 cm.

74

Wright & Jackson, Savannah

[Business card] of Wright & Jackson, factors and commission merchants, Bay street, Savannah, Georgia . . . [Savannah, 1861.] Card. 6½ x 10 cm.

Medicine

75

Marshall, C. K.

. . . Help for the wounded – an important proposition . . . [Signed:] C. K. Marshall. [Richmond, 1864.] Broadside, 30 x 16 cm.

At head of title: For the Enquirer.
Dated: Richmond, Jan. 12, 1864.
Printed in two columns.

76

[Nightingale, Florence]

Directions for cooking by troops, in camp and hospital, prepared for the Army of Virginia, and published by order of the Surgeon

General. Richmond, Va.: Printed by Ritchie & Dunnavant. 1861. 14 p. 15½ cm.

Broadside Verse

77

G., M. T.

Lines on the death of Joseph H. McCleskey, of the Athens Guards, who fell at Malvern Hill, in the battle below Richmond, July 1st, 1862. . . . [Signed:] M. T. G. [Athens, Ga., 1862.] Broadside, 32½ x 9.5 cm.

Dated: Athens, Geo. Oct. 24, 1862.

Play-Bills and Entertainments

78

Pic nic. You are respectfully solicited to attend a pic nic at Mrs. Perry's bridge, near Hatchechubbee, Mobile and Girard Railroad, on Saturday, 25th May, 1861. Managers. S. Woolfolk, H. P. Lockett, W. J. Williams, L. S. Thompson, William Perry, T. J. Wilkerson, W. R. Wilkerson, J. B. Denson. [Columbus, Ga.? 1861.] Broadside, 17½ x 10½ cm.

Songsters and Musical Instruction

79

Third edition of the Bonnie blue flag song book published by Blackmar & Bro., Augusta, Ga. . . . Macon, Ga.: Burke, Boykin & Co.'s Steam Printing House. 1863, c.1862. 32 p. 13 x 9 cm.

Contents on verso of cover-title. "The Irishman's shanty" on inside of back wrapper; "Catalogue of popular songs, with piano accompaniment, published by Blackmar & Bro., Augusta, Ga." on back wrapper.

Books and Publishing

80

DeBow's Review

[Circular letter, n. p., 1862] Broadside, 20 x 12 cm.

Announcement of change to bi-monthly instead of monthly issues of the Review.

Dated April 1, 1862.

Sheet Music

81*

. . . I would like to change my name. A favorite encore song, composed by Theod. von La Hache. New Orleans, Blackmar & Co. [c.1862] 5 p.

At head of title: Third edition. To his pupil, Miss Eliza Poitevent.

Catalogue on verso of p. 5.

82

Lorena. Written by Rev. H. D. L. Webster. Music by J. P. Webster. Macon, Ga., John W. Burke, n. d. [5] p.

Lithographed by R. H. Howell, Milledgeville, Ga.

83

Maryland! My Maryland! A patriotic song, written by James R. Randall; music by a lady of Baltimore. Augusta, Ga., Blackmar & Bro.; New-Orleans, Blackmar & Co. [c.1862]. [5] p.

Catalogue on verso of p. 5.

The type of the title is set differently from that in the title of Crandall 3642. The catalogue on verso of p. 5 is different from that of Crandall 3642.

84*

. . . Missouri! or, A voice from the South, written, composed and sung at his personation concerts, by Harry Macarthy. New Orleans: Blackmar & Co.; Augusta, Ga., Blackmar & Bro. [c.1861]. 3 p.

At head of title: Seventeenth edition.

Catalogue on verso of p. 3.

85*

Our first president quickstep, by P. Rivinac. New Orleans, A. E. Blackmar & Bro. [c.1861]. 7 p.

Portrait of President Davis on cover.

86*

. . . Retour du printemps: or, Return of spring. Polka brillante pour piano, par Theodore Moelling New Orleans, A. E. Blackmar & Bro. [etc., etc.] n. d. 9 p.

At head of title: Southern edition.

87*

. . . Secession quick step, by Herman L. Schreiner. Macon, Ga., John C. Schreiner & Sons, n. d. 6 p.

Flag with thirteen stars and rattlesnake on cover; overprinted on flag: The South, the whole South, and nothing but the South. Noli me tangere!

Possibly printed before the secession of Georgia.

88*

. . . The volunteer! or, It is my country's call! written, composed and sung at his personation concerts, by Harry Macarthy. Augusta, Ga., Blackmar & Bro.; New-Orleans, Blackmar & Co. [c. 1861]. 5 p.

At head of title: To the Orleans cadets.

Catalogue on verso of p. 5.

Differs from both Crandall 3925 and 3926 in the type setting of the title, in the contents of the catalogue, and the identifying phrase after Macarthy's name.

89

Why do I love thee, song. Words by Alf Burnett. Composed and dedicated to Miss Claudia Boddie of Jackson, Miss., by Charlie Ward. Columbia, S. C., B. Duncan & Co., Lithographers, n. d. [3] p.

Education and Educational Institutions

90*

South Carolina College

Treasurer's report to the honorable the board of trustees of the South Carolina College, November 1, 1862. Columbia, S. C.: Charles P. Pelham State, [*sic.*] Printer. 1862. 14, [2] p. incl. tables. 22 cm.

91

University High School, Athens, Georgia

University High School, Athens, Georgia. Athens, Ga.: Franklin Job Office Power-Press Print, 1864. 8 p. 14½ cm.

Textbooks

92*

Fleming, Robert

The revised elementary spelling book. The elementary spelling book, revised and adapted to the youth of the Southern Confederacy, interspersed with Bible readings on domestic slavery. By Rev. Robert Fleming. Twenty-sixth thousand. Atlanta, Ga.: J. J. Toon & Co., Publishers. Franklin Steam Printing House. 1863. 168 p. 17 cm.

At foot of imprint: Edition> <40,000.

Miscellaneous Religious Writings

93*

To the people of the Southern Confederacy. . . . n. p. [186-.] Broadside, 25½ x 20 cm.

A plea for strict observance of the Sabbath.

Church Publications

94

Baptist Church. North Carolina. Three Fork Association.

Minutes of the twenty-third annual session of the Three Fork Baptist Association, held with the church at Ebenezer, Watauga County, North Carolina, September 4th and 5th days, 1863. [n. p. 1863.] [4] p. 20½ cm.

95*

Protestant Episcopal Church. Diocese of Georgia.

To the clergy of the Diocese of Georgia. . . . [Savannah, 1861]. Broadside, 18½ x 14½ cm.

Sets Sunday, July 28, 1861, as a day of thanksgiving and praise.

Dated and signed: Given under my hand this July 24th, 1861. Stephen Elliott, Bishop of the Diocese of Georgia.

Tracts

96*

. . . Bread upon the waters; or, A true story of Lucknow. [Macon, Ga.? 186-.] 5, [1,2] p. 13 cm.

At head of title: Evangelical Tract Society, Petersburg, Va. No. 137.

On verso of p. 5: The Christian panopoly [*sic*]. At foot of this page: Soldiers' Tract Association, M. E. Church, South, Macon. Ga.

The last leaf is: . . . The swearer's prayer. Caption title. At head of title: Soldier's [*sic*] Tract Association, Macon, Ga. No. 2.

97*

. . . Kind words to a wounded soldier. [Published by the South Carolina Tract Society. Printed by Evans & Cogswell, No. 3 Broad Street, Charleston, S. C. 186-.] 12 p. 18 cm.

Caption title.

At head of title: No. 59.

98

. . . Soldiers in hospital; or, Come to Christ. [Published by the South Carolina Tract Society. Printed by Evans & Cogswell, No. 3 Broad Street, Charleston, S. C. 186-.] 7 p. 17½ cm.

Caption title.

At head of title: No. 97.

On verso of p. 7: List of tracts published by the South Carolina Tract Society. The list of tracts includes 102 titles.

Almanacs

99*

Grier's Southern almanac for the states of Georgia, South Carolina, Mississippi, Louisiana, Alabama, Tennessee. For the year of our Lord 1863, being the third after bissextile or leap-year, and the third of Southern independence, and (until 4th of July,) the eighty-seventh of the independence of the United States. Calculated for the latitude and meridian of Augusta, Ga., and will serve for the adjacent states, by T. P. Ashmore, of Americus, Ga. Published for the trade by F. H. Singer, Augusta, Ga. [1862.] 22, [1] p. 19 cm.

Additional imprint: Augusta, Ga.: A. Bleakley, Book-seller and Stationer.

100

Grier's Southern almanac for the states of Georgia, South Carolina, Mississippi, Louisiana, Alabama, Tennessee. For the year of our Lord 1863, being the third after bissextile or leap-year, and the third of Southern independence, and (until 4th of July,) the eighty-seventh of the independence of the United States. Calculated for the latitude and meridian of Augusta, Ga., and will serve for the adjacent states, by T. P. Ashmore, of Americus, Ga. Published for the trade by F. H. Singer, Augusta, Ga. [1862.] 22 p. 1 l. 19 cm.

Additional imprint: Augusta, Ga.: F. H. Singer Steam Printing Establishment.

101*

Grier's Southern almanac for the states of Georgia, South Carolina, Mississippi, Louisiana, Alabama, Tennessee. For the year of our Lord 1863, being the third after bissextile or leap-year, and the third of Southern independence, and (until 4th of July,) the eighty-seventh of the independence of the United States. Calculated for the latitude and meridian of Augusta, Ga., and will serve for the adjacent states, by T. P. Ashmore, of Americus, Ga. Published for the trade by F. H. Singer, Augusta, Ga. [1862.] 22, [1] p. 19 cm.

Additional imprint: Augusta, Ga.: Thos. Richards & Son, Booksellers and Stationers.

102

Grier's Southern almanac for the states of Georgia, South Carolina, Mississippi, Louisiana, Alabama, Tennessee. For the year of our Lord 1863, being the third after bissextile or leap-year, and the third of Southern independence, and (until 4th of July,) the eighty-seventh of the independence of the United States. Calculated for the latitude and meridian of Augusta, Ga., and will serve for the adjacent states, by T. P. Ashmore, of Americus, Ga. Published for the trade by F. H. Singer, Augusta, Ga. [1862.] 22, [1] 17½ cm.

Additional imprint: Savannah, Ga.: E. Knapp & Co., Book and Stationers' Warehouse.

103*

. . . Grier's Southern almanac for the year of our Lord 1864 being bissextile or leap-year. The fourth of the war for separation, and (until the fourth of July,) the eighty-eighth of the independence of the United States. Calculated for the latitude and meridian of Augusta, Ga. Lat. 33 deg. 30 m. N.: Long. 81 deg. 58 m. W. and will serve for all adjacent states. By T. P. Ashmore, of Americus, Ga. Published for the trade by F. H. Singer, Augusta, Ga. [1863.] 23 p. 19 cm.

Additional imprint: Augusta, Ga.: A. Bleakley, Books, Stationery, &c.

Previously Recorded Confederate Imprints

The numbers in this record refer to items in Boston Athenaeum, *Confederate Imprints, A Check List Based Principally on the Collection of the Boston Athenaeum* (Boston: The Boston Athenaeum, 1955), 2 v., and Richard Harwell, *More Confederate Imprints* (Richmond: The Virginia State Library, 1957), 2 v. Items in the first bibliography are known as "Crandall Numbers," those in the second as "Harwell Numbers." The Harwell numbers were devised to interfile with the Crandall numbers and can be distinguished by their being a combination of numbers separated by a short dash, e.g. 106-1. Numbers followed by a letter (e.g. 658R) are Harwell revisions of Crandall numbers.

1
5-1*
6
7*
8*
10
12
14
15
16* (Variant: 100p.)
17*
18*
19*
20*
21*
22*
23*
24*
28
29*
31
32-1*
35*
37*
41*
42*
43
44*
48
53*
58*
59*
60*
61*
66*
68*
69*
70*
71*
72*
72-1*
72-21*
72-27*
72-28*
73*
76*
77*
78*
79
87*
89*
90*
92*
92-1*
100-2*
102*
103*
108*
110*
115*
126*
127-1*
129*
130
133*
134*
134-1*
135*
136*
137*
138*
139*
140*
141*
146*
148*
149*
154*
155*
161*

163*
164*
166*
166-2*
166-3
167*
168*
169*
170*
171*
173*
174*
175*
177*
178*
179*
180*
183*
184*
187*
188*
189*
191*
192*
192-1*
194*
196*
202*
203*
204*
206*
209*
215*
216*
218*
219*
220*
221*
222*
225*
227*
230*
232*
235*
236*
237*
238*
240*
242*
248*
252*
258*
262*
265*
274*
277*
278*
280*
281*
282*
283*
284*
285*
286*
287*
288*
289*
292*
295*
296*
297*
298*
301*
302*
304*
305*
308*
309*
313*
314*
315*
316*
318*
319*
320*
320-1*
321*
322*
323*
324*
325*
327
329*
330*
334*
336*
338*
339*
340*
342*
346*
346-1
347*
348*
349*
350*
351*
352*
353*
354*
355*
356*
357*
358*
360*
362*
363*
364*
365*
366*
368*
370*
371*
372*
374*
375*
376*
377*
378*
379*
380*
381*
382*
384*
385*

386*
388*
389*
390*
391*
392*
393*
398*
399*
400*
401*
403*
404*
406*
406-1*
407*
407-1*
409*
412*
413*
414
415
416
417
418
419
421
422
423
424
426
427
428
429
430*
431*
432*
434*
435*
436*
437*
438*
439*
440*
441*
442*
443*
444*
445*
449*
450*
451*
452*
453*
454*
455*
457*
458*
459*
460*
461*
462*
463*
464*
465*
467*
468*
469*
470*
471*
472*
473*
474*
475*
476*
477*
478*
479*
480*
481*
482*
483*
484*
485*
486*
487*
488*
489*
490*
491*
492*
493*
494*
495*
496*
497*
497-2*
498
499*
500*
501*
502*
505*
506*
507
508*
509*
510*
511*
512*
513*
514*
515*
516*
517*
518*
519*
520*
521*
522*
523*
524*
525*
526
527*
528*
529*
530*
531*
532*
535*
536*
537*
538
539*

540
541*
542*
543
544*
545*
547*
548*
549*
550*
551*
553*
554*
555*
556*
557*
558*
559*
560*
562*
(Apr. 7, 15, 1862; Dec. 28, 1863; Jan. 11, 25. 1864; Nov. 7, 1864; Jan. 9, 1865.)
564*
569*
569-1*
570*
575*
575-1*
577*
578*
581*
583*
584*
585*
586*
587*
588*
591*
592*
593*
597*
598*

599*
600*
601*
605
607
608*
609*
610*
611
612*
613*
614*
615*
617*
618*
620*
622*
623*
624*
626*
627*
628*
629*
631*
632*
633*
634*
635*
637*
641
649-1
658 R* (No. 1)
659 R*
(Nos. 62, 66, 68, 71, 78, 87 (8-21-63), 87 (9-10-63), 88, 90, 93, 97, 100, 101, 105, 109, 112)
669*
670
675 (No. 12)
678*
684-1* (No. 2)
688 R* (No. 3)
697*

698
702-1* (No. 14)
717-1* (No. 9)
719-1*
(Nos. 4, 6, 10-12)
719-2* (Nos. 9- 18)
719-3* (No. 5)
719-5* (Nos. 3, 12 - 14, 18, 19)
723-1*
726*
728*
734 (No. 5)
737 (No. 1)
749
749 (Variant Printing)
756
760
762
768 (No. 63)
769-1
769-2
773
773-6 (No. 41)
774 R (Nos. 4, 6)
782*
786-1*
797-2 (Nos. 7, 8)
798
(Nos. 42, 62-65, 67-69, 71-74.)
801 (No. 4)
810
813*
815*
816*
818-2*
821*
823-1
824*
827*
828*
829*
833*

834*
835*
836*
837*
838*
839*
(3 variant covers: brown, green, white)
841
848*
848-1*
849
850-1*
850-3*
861*
862
863
864*
865*
866
874*
878
881*
882
888*
895
896*
897*
898*
899*
900*
901*
902-1*
906*
916
917*
919*
923*
924*
925*
950-1*
971*
994
1008-1*
1008-2*
1011*
1023*
1031-1*
1032
1044
1057*
1058
1059
1060*
1066*
1067
1069*
1069-1*
1069-3*
1080-1*
1083
1091*
1092*
1094*
1096*
1098
1099
1100*
1101*
1103*
1104*
1105*
1106*
1107
1108*
1109*
1110*
1111*
1112*
1113*
1114*
1115*
1116*
1117*
1119*
1120*
1122*
1123*
1124*
1125*
1126
1128
1129
1130
1132
1133
1134
1137*
1140*
1141
1141-1*
1142-1*
1143*
1147*
1149
1150*
1151*
1152*
1153*
1156*
1157*
1160
1161*
1163*
1164*
1165*
1167-1*
1168*
1172*
1173-1*
1174*
1178*
1180*
1184*
1185*
1186*
1187*
1188*
1189*
1193*
1197*
1202*
1203*
1205*

(No. 1 (Feb.), 1 (Mar.), 2-14, 19, 20, 24, 25)
1206*
1207
1210*
1211
1212*
1235*
1236-1
1245
1254*
(1-21 papers, 1-21 memos; Jan. 31, May 30, Je. 12, Aug. 17, Oct. 8, Dec. 7, Jan. 4, '64, Mar. 14, Apr. 30, Nov. 14.)
1255*
1263
1264*
1268*
1271*
1274*
1275*
1278*
1279*
1280*
1284*
1285*
1287*
1290*
1291*
1294
1295*
1296*
1298*
1299*
1300*
1301*
1303*
1304*
1305*
1306*
1307*
1308*
1309*
1310*
1311*
1312*
1313
1314
1315
1316
1317*
1318*
1319*
1321*
1322*
1323*
1324*
1327*
1328*
1330
1331
1332*
1333*
1340*
1342*
1343
1344*
1347* (No. 17)
1348*
(Nos. 1-4, 6, 10, 12, 19-21, 24, 26, 28-30, 34-40, 52, 63, 64, 68, 69, 71-73, 75, 77-85, 87, 90-93, 95-98, 100-11.), also variant printing of 106 and 107.
1349* (Nos. 1-164)
1350* (Nos. 1-87)
1351* (Nos. 5-9, 11)
1357*
1358*
1359*
1362*
1363*
1364*
1365*
1367*
1372*
1374*
1375*
1376
1377*
1378*
1379*
1381*
1382
1383*
1385*
1387*
1388*
1389
1390*
1390-1*
1391
1393*
1396*
1397
1399*
1403
1406*
1408*
1411
1412*
1414*
1415*
1416
1418* (Incomplete)
1419*
1421*
1423*
1425*
1426*
1427*
1429*
1431*
1432*

1433*
1434*
1435*
1436*
1437-1*
1444*
1448-3
1450-2*
1450-3*
1451*
1455*
1455-2*
1456
1457*
1459*
1461*
1462*
1465*
1466*
1466-1*
1466-2*
1467*
1468*
1469*
1469-1*
1473-2*
1482*
1482-1*
1484*
1484-2
1485* (Incomplete)
1486*
1487*
1496*
1497*
1498*
1499*
1500
1502*
1503*
1504*
1504
(Variant in cover and size.)
1504-1*
1504-2*
1505*
1505-1*
1509*
1509-1*
1510*
1511*
1513*
1514*
1514-1*
1516-2*
1517
1518*
1519
1520
1521
1522
1523*
1524*
1527
1528
1529
1531
1531-2*
1531-3*
1531-4*
1533
1535
1538
1539*
1540
1541
1542
1543
1544*
1545*
1546
1547
1548
1549
1550
1551*
1552*
1556
1557
1558
1559
1561-1
1561-2*
1561-4*
1561-5*
1561-6*
1561-7*
1562
1563*
1563 (52 p.)
1564
1567
1568
1569
1571
1573
1573-1
1574
1574-1*
1578
1580
1580-1*
1581
1581-1
(2, 4, 5, 8)
1582 (1,3)
1583
1584
1586-1*
1588
1589
1594-1*
1594-2*
1594-3*
1594-4*
1594-5*
1596-1
1601
1603-1*
1606
1609
1610
1611

2617*
2618
2620 (Books 3 & 4 only)
2623
2625
2629*
2632
2634* (Incomplete)
2635
2636
2637*
2638*
2641*
2643*
2645
2647*
2649*
2650*
2654*
2661
2662*
2664*
2665*
2670
2676*
2679*
2685
2687*
2697*
2697-1*
2701*
2712
2720
2728*
2738*
2739-1*
2750*
2751
2758*
2762
2763*
2767*

2769*
2774*
2778
2779
2780*
2781-2*
2783*
2784*
2785*
2787*
2792
2794
2804*
2819-1
2821
2830*
2831
2834*
2835*
2839*
2845*
2848*
2859*
2861*
2864
2866*
2866-1
2866-2
2870*
2873
2875-1*
2877*
2882*
2886*
2888
2898
2902*
2904-2
2906
2907
2907-1*
2911-1*
2917-1*
2918*
2919*

2926*
2927*
2928-1*
2928-2*
2929
2930-3*
2934*
2937-1*
2942-3*
2962
2989
2990
2991
2992*
2995*
3000
3012*
3017
3018
3028*
3031*
3033*
3036*
3041
3042*
3044*
3045-1
3047
3048*
3053
3054*
3060*
3062
3063*
3066*
3069
3070*
3075*
3082
3095*
3096*
3097
3101
3104
3105*

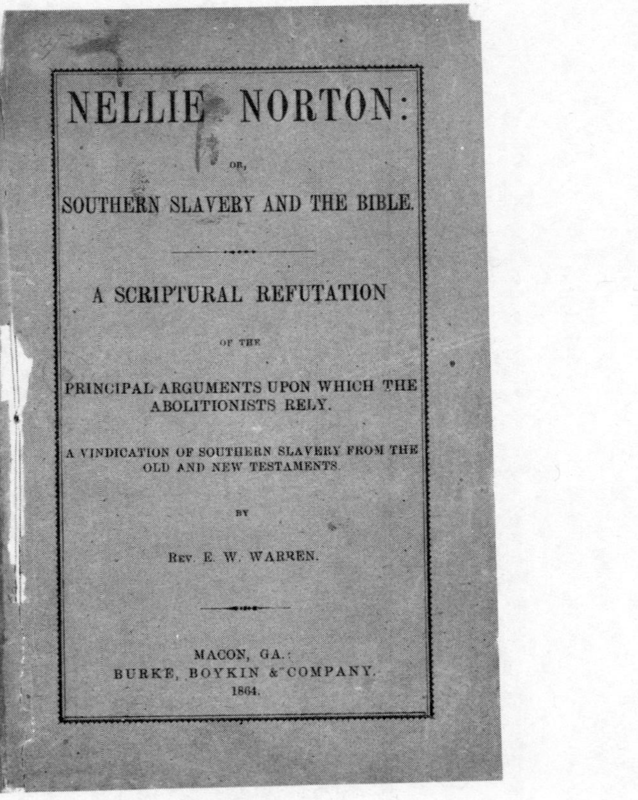

NELLIE NORTON:

OR,

SOUTHERN SLAVERY AND THE BIBLE.

A SCRIPTURAL REFUTATION

OF THE

PRINCIPAL ARGUMENTS UPON WHICH THE ABOLITIONISTS RELY.

A VINDICATION OF SOUTHERN SLAVERY FROM THE OLD AND NEW TESTAMENTS.

BY

REV. E. W. WARREN.

MACON, GA.:
BURKE, BOYKIN & COMPANY.
1864.

Crandall 3113

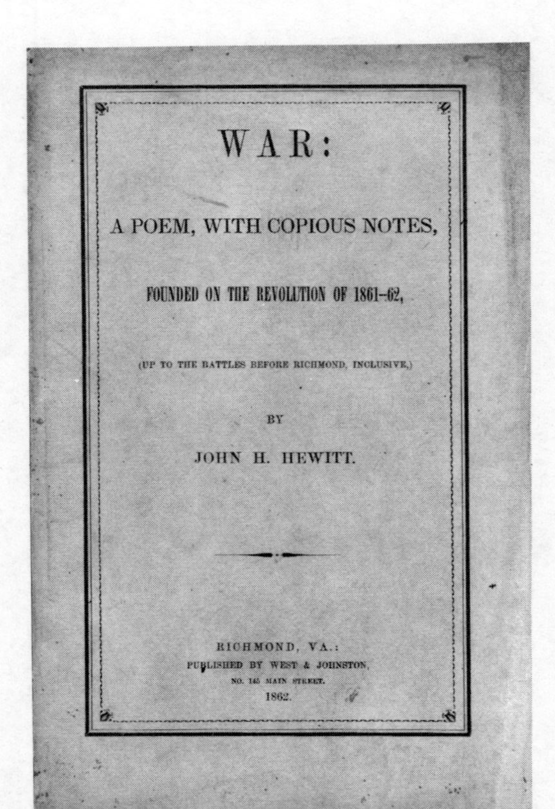

WAR:

A POEM, WITH COPIOUS NOTES,

FOUNDED ON THE REVOLUTION OF 1861–62,

(UP TO THE BATTLES BEFORE RICHMOND, INCLUSIVE,)

BY

JOHN H. HEWITT.

RICHMOND, VA.:
PUBLISHED BY WEST & JOHNSTON,
NO. 145 MAIN STREET.
1862.

Crandall 3140

THE

CATECHISM

OF THE

Protestant Episcopal Church

IN THE

CONFEDERATE STATES.

RALEIGH:
OFFICE OF "THE CHURCH INTELLIGENCER."
1862.

Harwell 4260-2

THE

JACK MORGAN

SONGSTER.

COMPILED BY A

CAPT. IN GEN. LEE'S ARMY.

RALEIGH, N. C.,
BRANSON & FARRAR,
FAYETTEVILLE STREET.

1864.

Crandall 3256

3106* (Vols. 2-4)
3108
3112
3113*
3115*
3126*
3129*
3130*
3138*
3140*
3141*
3143-1*
3144*
3147*
3154*
3157-4*
3164*
3210-1*
3256*
3261*
3263*
3284
3292*
3294*
3294 (Variant printing; color different)
3297
3298*
3299*
3301*
3302*
3303*
3304*
3305*
3306*
3310*
3312*
3316*
3320*
3323*
3324*
3325*
3327*
3328*
3330
3332*
3337*
3339*
3340-1*
3340-2*
3341
3342*
3345*
3348*
3349*
3350*
3350 (Variant printing; paper different)
3351*
3351-1*
3352*
3352 (Variant printing; paper different)
3356*
3357*
3360*
3363*
3364
3368*
3370*
3371*
3372*
3374
3375*
3381*
3383*
3385
3386*
3387*
3390*
3396*
3401
3401-1*
3402*
3405*
3407*
3408
3411*
3413*
3415
3416-1
3422*
3423*
3427*
3427-1*
3430*
3431*
3432*
3434*
3435*
3436*
3436 (Variant as listed)
3438*
3439
3442*
3445*
3446*
3448
3449*
3450*
3452*
3453*
3458*
3462*
3474*
3476
3477*
3481*
3484*
3485 (Incomplete)
3486
3488*
3489*
3490
3494
3496
3502*
3503
3510*
3511*
3514

3515*
3517*
3521*
3525*
3526*
3528*
3530*
3532*
3532-2*
3533*
3536*
3538*
3541
3542*
3543
3544*
3546
3547*
3548*
3550
3551*
3552*
3553*
3555*
3558
3559*
3562*
3570*
3573*
3575*
3576*
3577*
3582*
3583*
3587
3587-1*
3588*
3589*
3590*
3591*
3594*
3600*
3601*
3601-1*
3602*
3605*
3606
3607*
3609*
3610*
3611
3612
3613*
3614*
3621* (Purple ink)
3621 (Magenta ink)
3622*
3628*
3631*
3634*
3635
3636*
3636 (Variant printing; paper different)
3638*
3639*
3640*
3641*
3642*
3643*
3650*
3653*
3653-1*
3658* (Black ink)
3658 (Blue ink)
3659*
3660* (Black ink)
3660* (Blue ink)
3662*
3666*
3668
3669*
3670*
3671*
3676* (Brown & blue ink.)
3676* (Green & blue ink.)
3677*
3679*
3686*
3687*
3689*
3692*
3693
3694*
3694* (Variant as listed)
3697*
3698*
3702*
3703*
3705
3706-1*
3707*
3707 (Variant printing; paper different)
3710
3712*
3713*
3714
3716*
3720*
3733*
3736*
3737
3738
3739*
3744
3744-1*
3750*
3753
3757
3759*
3760
3762*
3764*
3766*
3770
3775
3776*
3776-1*

3776-2*
3778*
3779*
3780*
3781*
3782
3783
3785
3787*
3788*
3793*
3793* (Variant as listed)
3794*
3797*
3800*
3801
3802*
3804*
3805*
3806*
3807*
3808*
3812
3813*
3814
3816*
3818*
3819*
3823*
3824*
3829*
3830*
3832*
3833*
3838*
3839*
3840
3845
3846
3849*
3850*
3851*
3853
3855*
3860
3863*
3868*
3869*
3871*
3874*
3875*
3876*
3878*
3882*
3885*
3887*
3888*
3892*
3893*
3894*
3895
3898*
3901*
3909*
3910*
3911*
3912*
3913*
3914*
3917*
3920 (Incomplete)
3922*
3925
3926*
3927*
3927 (Variant as listed)
3930*
3930* (Variant printing; catalogue on verso of p. 5 different)
3933*
3934*
3935*
3943*
3944*
3945*
3947* (Purple-gray ink)
3947 (Blue ink)
3948*
3949*
3950*
3953*
3954*
3955
3956*
3957* (Blue ink)
3957 (Green ink)
3959*
3960*
3961*
3961* (Variant as listed)
3962*
3963
3964*
3966*
3967*
3968*
3970*
3972*
3973
3975
3978*
3979
3980*
3981*
3982*
3982* (Variant printing; lithographed title page different.)
3983*
3984*
3990*
4002
4004*
4006*
4008
4008-1*
4013

4016-1*
4023-1*
4024-1*
4026*
4027-1*
4027-3*
4029*
4030*
4031
4032*
4032
(Variant printing; binding different)
4033*
4034*
4036*
4040*
4048*
4054*
4055*
4059*
4060*
4061*
4063*
4067*
4068*
4069*
4069
(Different decoration on cover title)
4070*
4071
4077*
4083*
4085*-R
4087*
4089*
4093*
4101*
4105*
4107*
4110*
4120*
4122*
4123*
4133*
4136*
4137*
4138*
4140
4142
4143*
4144
4145*
4146
4147
4149
4150
4151*
4152
4153*
4160-1*
4162-1*
4168*
4170*
4171*
4175*
4176*
4178*
4179
4186*
(Incomplete)
4192*
4194*
4196*
4201*
4215*
4222
4227
4229*
4232
4234*
4240*
4241
4242-1*
4243-1*
4243-2*
4247*
4247-1*
4248*
4254-1*
4254-4*
4255-1*
4257-2*
4258*
4260-2*
4261*
4265*
4265-1*
4265-2*
4273*
4275*
4277*
4279-1*
4282
4286*
4288*
4289*
4309*
4321*
4322*
4323*
4336*
4337*
4338*
4338-1*
4342*
4343*
4344*
4345*
4352*
4352-4*
4354-3*
4354-26*
4358-2*
4359*
4360*
4360-1*
4360-2*
4361-1*
4361-2*
4361-3*
4361-4*

4361-8*
4361-9*
4361-10*
4361-11*
4361-12*
4361-13*
4361-14*
4361-15*
4363*
4365*
4366*
4367*
4368*
4373*
4375*
4376*
4384*
4385*
4386*
4388*
4389*
4390*
4391*
4418*
4421*
4422* (Incomplete)
4423*
4423-2*
4424*
4425*
4431-4*
4441*
4442*
4442-1*
4446*
4448*
4449*
4451*
4452*
4454*
4454-2*
4454-3*
4454-4*
4454-5*
4455*
4456*
4457*
4457-1*
4461* (Incomplete)
4467*
4468*
4473*
4473-1*
4473-2*
4475
4476*
4478*
4479*
4480*
4481*
4483*
4497*
4498*
4501*
4502*
4503*
4506-1*
4511*
4512*
4513*
4515-5*
4515-6*
4516
4517
4518
4519
4520
4521
4522*
4529
4530
4531
4532
4536*
4556*
4564*
4565*
4566
4567*
4578*
4578-1*
4579*
4586
4590*
4591*
4597*
4600*
4601*
4601-1*
4608*
4612*
4616*
4620-1*
4627
4645*
4674*
4689*
4698*
4727*
4739*
4753*
4754*
4769*
4790*
4813*
4840*
4857*
4858*
4872
4883*
4884*
4890*
4892*
4897*
4902*
4918*
4919-1*
4947-1
4948
4949*
4954*
4955-1*
4961*

4964
4967*
4971*
4971-1*
4972*
4972-1*
4977*
4979*
4980*
4984
4987
4990*
4992*
4995-1*
4996*
4997*
4998
4999
5001
5020
5049*
5059*
5084-8
5084-9
5084-10
5084-11*
5084-12
5085
5092
5093*
5102*
5112*
5113*

Appendix

Periodicals

5123*

THE AGE. Richmond, Va. 1864-65.
Vol. 1, No. 1-2, Jan. & Feb., 1864.

5152*

THE COUNTRYMAN. Turnwold, Ga. 1862-65.
1862: Sept. 29, Oct. 6, 13, 20, Nov. 3, 10, 17, 24, Dec. 1, 8, 15.
1863: July 7.
1864: May 3, 10, June 7, Sept. 13.
1865: Jan. 3, 10, 31; Feb. 7, 28, Mar. 7.

5183*

DE BOW'S REVIEW, and Industrial Resources, Statistics, etc. New Orleans, La., and Charleston, S. C., 1861-64.
1861: Vol. 5, New series, No. 1, 2, 3, 5-6; Jan., Feb., Mar., May & June;
Vol. 6, New series, No. 1, 2, 3, 4-5, 6; July, Aug., Sept., Oct.-Nov., Dec.

5232*

THE NORTH CAROLINA JOURNAL OF EDUCATION. Greensboro, N. C. 1861-64.
Vol. 5, No. 3, 9; Mar., Sept., 1862.
Vol. 6, No. 4; Apr. 1863.

5239*

THE RECORD OF NEWS, HISTORY AND LITERATURE. Richmond, Va. 1863.
Vol. 1, No. 9, Aug. 13, 1863.

5262*

THE SOUTHERN EPISCOPALIAN: A monthly periodical. Charleston, S. C. 1861.
Vol. 7, No. 12. Mar., 1861.
Vol. 8, No. 1-9, Apr.-Dec., 1861.

5263*

SOUTHERN FIELD AND FIRESIDE. Augusta, Ga. 1861-1864.

1861: Feb. 2, 23, Mar. 2, 9, 23, 30, Apr. 6, 13, 20, 27, May 4, 11, 25, June 1, 8, 15, 22, 29, July 13, 20, Aug. 10, 17, 24, 31, Sept. 7, 14, 21, 28, Oct. 5, 12, 19, 26, Nov. 2, 9, 16, Dec. 7, 13, 28.

1862: Jan. 4, 11, 18, Feb. 8, May 24, June 1.

1863: Jan. 3, 10, 17, 25, 31, Feb. 7, 14, 21, 28, Mar. 7, 14, 21, 28, Apr. 4, 11, 18, 25, May 2, 9, 16, 23, 30, June 6, 13, 20, 27, July 4, 11, 18, 25, Aug. 1, 8, 15, 21, 29, Sept. 5, 12, 19, 26.

1864.: Jan. 2, 9, 16, 23, 30, Feb. 6, 13, 20, 27, Mar. 6, 12, 19, 26, Apr. 2, 9, 16, 23, May 7, 14, 21, 28, June 4, 11, 18, 25, July 2, 9, 16, 23, 30, Aug. 6, 13, 20, 27, Sept. 3, 10, 17, 24, Oct. 1, 8, 15, 22, 29, Nov. 5, 19, 26, Dec. 10, 17, 24.

1865: Jan. 14, 28, Feb. 4.

5265

THE SOUTHERN ILLUSTRATED NEWS. Richmond, Va. 1862-1864.

Vol. 1, No. 26, Mar. 7, 1863.

5266*

THE SOUTHERN LITERARY MESSENGER; devoted to every department of literature and the fine arts. Richmond, Va. 1861-64.

1861: Vol. 32, No. 1-6, Jan.-June, 1861, Vol. 33, 1-6, July-Dec., 1861. Complete.

1862: Vol. nos. confused. Jan.-Dec. Complete.

1863: Jan.-Dec. Complete.

1864. Jan.-June.

5267

SOUTHERN MEDICAL AND SURGICAL JOURNAL. Augusta, Ga. 1861.

Vol. 17, New series, 1861, Jan.-Dec.

5268*

THE SOUTHERN MONTHLY. Memphis, Tenn., etc. 1861-1862.

Vol. 1, No. 1-2, Sept. & Oct., 1861.

5270

THE SOUTHERN PRESBYTERIAN REVIEW, conducted by an association of ministers, in Columbia, South Carolina. Columbia, S. C. 1863. Vol. 16, No. 3, April, 1864. (pages missing)

5271

SOUTHERN PUNCH. Richmond, Va. 1863-1864.

Vol. 1, No. 25, Feb. 6, 1864.

Not Listed in Crandall or Harwell.

SOUTHERN CULTIVATOR. Augusta, Ga. and Athens, Ga. 1861-65.
1861: Vol. 19, No. 1-12, Jan.-Dec. 1861. Complete.
1862: Vol. 20, No. 1-12, Jan.-Dec., 1862. Complete.
1863: Vol. 21, No. 1-12, Jan.-Dec., 1863. Complete.
1864: Vol. 22, No. 1-15, Jan.-Dec., 1864. Complete.
Note: Issued weekly for brief period in Nov. & Dec., 1864.

THE ASSEMBLY REPORTER, THE SOUTHERN PRESBYTERIAN. -EXTRA. Augusta, Ga.
December, 1861. Elam Sharpe & Co.
1861: No. 1-11, Dec. 5, 6, 7, 9, 10, 11, 12, 13, 14, 16, 17.

THE SAVANNAH JOURNAL OF MEDICINE. Savannah, Ga. 1861.
Vol. 4, No. 5-6, Sept. & Oct., 1861.

THE SOUTHERN TEACHER; A Journal of Home and School Education. Montgomery, Ala.
Vol. 2, No. 6, Jan., 1861.
Vol. 2, No. 10, May, 1861.

Newspapers

ALABAMA

Mobile

5219*

MOBILE EVENING NEWS. 1862.
1862: Apr. 25.

Montgomery

5222

MONTGOMERY DAILY ADVERTISER. 1861.
1861: Sept. 10.

[Not listed]*

MONTGOMERY WEEKLY ADVERTISER. 1863.
1863: May 6.

Selma

[Not listed]

SOUTHERN OBSERVER. 1864.
1864: Sept. 23.

GEORGIA

Athens

[Not listed]
SOUTHERN BANNER. 1861-1865. Incomplete.
218 issues.

[Not listed]
SOUTHERN WATCHMAN. 1861-1864. Incomplete.
11 issues.

Atlanta

5174
THE COMMONWEALTH. 1862.
1862: Aug. 17.

5163
THE DAILY INTELLIGENCER. 1863-1864. Incomplete.
50 issues.

[Not listed]
THE GEORGIA LITERARY AND TEMPERANCE CRUSADER. 1861. Incomplete.
19 issues.

5211
MEMPHIS DAILY APPEAL. 1863-1864. Incomplete.
8 issues.

5260
SOUTHERN CONFEDERACY. 1861-1864. Incomplete.
352 issues.

Augusta

5164
AUGUSTA CHRONICLE (DAILY). 1861-1865. Incomplete.
41 issues.

5143
AUGUSTA CHRONICLE (WEEKLY). 1861-1865. Incomplete.
210 issues.

[Not listed]
AUGUSTA EVENING DISPATCH. 1861. Incomplete.
9 issues.

5158
THE DAILY CONSTITUTIONALIST. 1861-1865. Incomplete.
89 issues

5258
SOUTHERN CHRISTIAN ADVOCATE. 1862-1864. Incomplete.
16 issues

5269

SOUTHERN PRESBYTERIAN. 1864.
1864: Nov. 3.

[Not listed]

SOUTHERN REPUBLIC. (DAILY) 1861. Incomplete.
5 issues.

5272

SOUTHERN REPUBLIC. (WEEKLY). 1861.
1861: June 5.

Columbus

5155

DAILY COLUMBUS ENQUIRER. 1861-1864. Incomplete.
998 issues.

[Not listed]

WEEKLY COLUMBUS ENQUIRER. 1862-1863. Incomplete.
101 issues

Greensboro

[Not listed]

CRUSADER. 1861.
1861: June 20 - Extra.

Griffin

[Not listed]

THE SOUTHERN UNION. 1861, 1863. Incomplete.
2 issues.

Macon

5208

THE MACON DAILY TELEGRAPH. 1861-1864. Incomplete.
22 issues.

[Not listed]

THE MACON WEEKLY TELEGRAPH. 1862. Incomplete.
4 issues.

[Not listed]*

THE MACON TELEGRAPH AND CONFEDERATE. 1865.
1865: Jan. 20.

5261

THE SOUTHERN CONFEDERACY. 1864. Incomplete.
2 issues.

Milledgeville

5150

FEDERAL UNION [SOUTHERN FEDERAL UNION: THE CONFEDERATE UNION - TITLE CHANGES] 1861-1865.
219 issues.

[Not listed]

SOUTHERN RECORDER (WEEKLY) 1861-1864.
134 issues.

Newnan

[Not listed]

WINCHESTER DAILY BULLETIN. 1863. Incomplete.
2 issues.

Sandersville

5133

CENTRAL GEORGIAN. 1861-1862. Incomplete.
70 issues.

Savannah

[Not listed]

SAVANNAH DAILY HERALD. 1865.
1865: Feb. 27.

5166

SAVANNAH DAILY MORNING NEWS. 1861-1862. Incomplete.
12 issues.

5247

THE SAVANNAH REPUBLICAN. 1862-1865. Incomplete
4 issues

[Not listed]*

SAVANNAH DAILY LOYAL GEORGIAN. 1864.
1864: Dec. 24.

Thomasville

[Not listed]

SOUTHERN ENTERPRISE. 1861. Incomplete.
2 issues

Washington

[Not listed]*

THE WASHINGTON INDEPENDENT
1863: Dec. 13.

NORTH CAROLINA

Charlotte

[Not listed]*

THE DAILY BULLETIN. 1865.
1865: Feb. 8

5177*

THE DAILY SOUTH CAROLINIAN. 1865.
1865: Mar. 25.
Note: This issue published in Charlotte, N. C.

SOUTH CAROLINA

Charleston

5135

THE CHARLESTON DAILY COURIER. 1864. Incomplete.
2 issues.

5136

THE CHARLESTON MERCURY. 1862.
1862: Feb. 25.

Columbia

5269

THE SOUTHERN PRESBYTERIAN. 1861.
1861: Oct. 26.
See Also: Augusta, Ga. Issue for Nov. 3, 1864 published in Augusta, Ga.

VIRGINIA

Norfolk

5182*

THE DAY BOOK (WEEKLY) 1862.
1862: May 7.

Richmond

5160

DAILY DISPATCH. 1861.
1861. July 4.

5176

DAILY RICHMOND EXAMINER. 1861-1862. Incomplete.
5 issues.

5245

DAILY RICHMOND WHIG. 1862. Incomplete.
6 issues.

5175

THE DAILY RICHMOND ENQUIRER. 1863. Incomplete.
100 issues.

5244

RICHMOND ENQUIRER (SEMI-WEEKLY). 1863.
1863: Sept. 11.

[See 5245]*

THE RICHMOND WEEKLY WHIG. 1862. Incomplete.
2 issues.

WITHDRAWAL